Nature

Nature, numbers

1 **Match the two parts of the words.**

1 po — sect

2 mush — rds

      nd

3 in

4 bi — rooms

5 ro

6 clou — ds   ck

2 **Read and complete.**

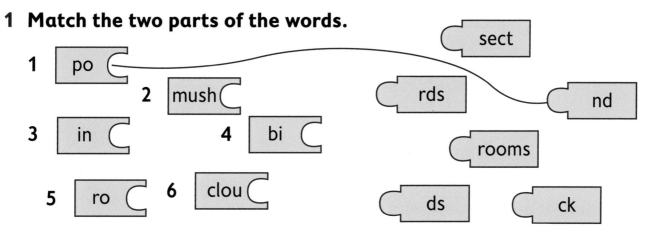

There are six spiders plus thirteen ants in the garden. That equals
_____ insects.
There are twelve books on nature in the library plus eight dictionaries.
That equals _____ books.
There are thirty children in the school minus twenty in the classroom
play. That equals _____ children in the playground.

3 **Complete the words.**

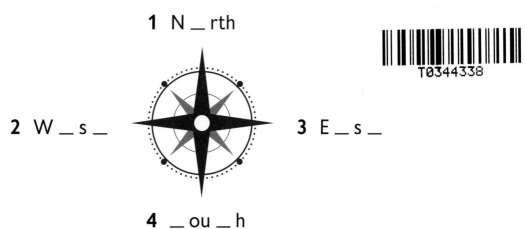

1 N _ rth

2 W _ s _

3 E _ s _

4 _ ou _ h

T0344338

How many …?

4 Unscramble the questions. Then answer.

1 many / are / flowers / there / How

_____?

_____.

2 rainbows / are / many / How / there

_____?

_____.

5 Read. Then find two questions and two answers.

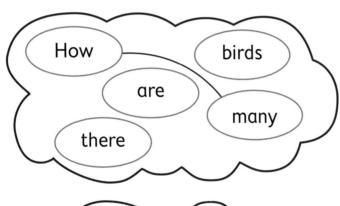

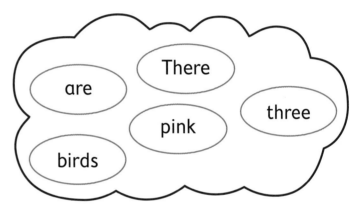

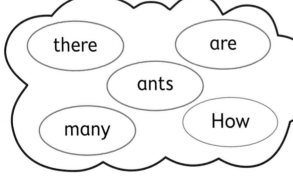

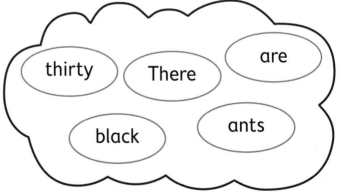

1 How many _____?

_____.

2 _____?

_____.

6 Look. Then read and match.

1
| Are there any insects? |

a
| Yes, there are.
There are three. |

2
| Is there a tree? |

b
| No, there aren't. |

3
| Are there any frogs? |

c
| Yes, there is.
There's one. |

7 Read and complete. Use *is, are, isn't* or *aren't*.

The frog

In my garden there <u>'s</u> a pond. It's not a big pond but there _____ some fish and frogs in it. I go to the pond to play with my boat. There _____ one frog that is my favourite. It swims next to my boat. Sometimes it jumps out of the pond onto the rocks. There _____ any clouds in the sky today. It is very hot, it _____ cold. There _____ three frogs there today.

1 Where is / are ...?

8 Unscramble the questions. Then look and answer.

1  she / Where / ? / is

_____

_____

2  are / ? / they / Where

_____

_____

3  go / you / holiday / Where / on / ? / do

_____

_____

4  ? / Where / they / are

_____

_____

9 What can you see at the library? Read and write.

| some | any |

1 There are _____ books.   2 There are _____ children.

3 There aren't _____ flowers.   4 There aren't _____ insects.

10 Look. What can you see? Write (✔) or (✗).

1 three trees   ✗

2 the sun   ☐

3 two rocks   ☐

4 two clouds   ☐

5 five flowers   ☐

6 six spiders   ☐

11 Now read.

In the picture, there are some flowers. Next to the flowers there are two rocks. There are nine ants on the rocks. Next to the rocks there are three trees. Behind the rocks there's a pond. The sun is in the sky. Next to the sun there are two big clouds. It is sunny and cloudy. Under the clouds there are five birds.

Read again. Then circle.

1 The (*rocks* / *birds*) are next to the flowers.

2 There are (*four* / *five*) birds.

3 The birds are (*under* / *next to*) the clouds.

4 There's a pond (*behind* / *next to*) the rocks.

5 It's (*windy* / *cloudy*).

Describing a picture

Remember!

There's one flower.   There are two flowers.

There's one ant.   There are six ants.

12 Draw a nature picture. Then write.

- What's in the picture?

- How many birds, ants and trees are there?

- Where are they?

Me

Parts of the body

1 Match. Then draw.

1 blue   **a** glasses

2 small   **b** eyes

3 blond   **c** hair

2 Read. Then circle.

1 broad (*hair / shoulders*)   2 strong (*eyes / arms*)

3 a flat (*arm / stomach*)   4 short (*fingernails / stomach*)

3 Look and write. Use words from the box.

| beard   moustache   chin   glasses |

1 round   2 short   3 black   4 small

_____   _____   _____   _____

4 Look and match.

1 bird

2 reptile

3 marsupial

a    **b**   **c**

5 Read and underline the mistakes. Then write.

<u>I got</u> black hair. My sister have got black hair, too. I hasn't got glasses. Have got you long hair?

I've got black

6 Draw. Then write about you. Use some of the words from the box.

have got   haven't got
short   nose   long
hair   chin   eyes   round
glasses   thick   neck
eyebrows   small

7 Draw lines in different colours. Make sentences.

I Jamie Claire and Stuart	have got has got	a big small green short black	beard eyes hair

8 Unscramble sentences. Then colour.

1 got / Jenny / hair / long / has / brown

Jenny has got long brown hair.

2 has / Steve / got / hair / short / black

_____

3 got / Helena / blue / has / eyes / small

_____

4 big / has / George / got / ears

_____

2 Have you got ... ?

9 Read. Then answer.

Personal information

Have you got long / short hair?	I've got
What colour hair have you got?	
What colour eyes have you got?	
Have you got glasses?	
Have you got a beard?	
Have you got big ears?	

10 Read. Then complete. Use *have / has got*.

Me

Hi, I'm Sally. This is a photo of my family. I <u>'ve</u> got one sister and one brother. I _____ got short hair, I've got long hair. In this photo, my brother has _____ a ball. He loves football. His name is Craig. My sister and mum _____ got long blond hair. We haven't _____ thick eyebrows but we _____ got small ears. My dad _____ got a beard or a moustache but my grandad has. I love my family!

11 Read. Then draw.

I'm Rita. I'm a woman.
I've got a small nose and
a big mouth. I've got long
eyelashes. I've got short
red hair and green eyes.
I've got brown glasses.
I've got a round chin and
a short neck.

I'm Andrew. I'm a man.
I've got a big nose and
a small mouth. I've got
thick eyebrows and thick
eyelashes. I've got long
grey hair and brown eyes.
I've got a grey moustache.
I've got a long neck.

12 Read again. Then write *R* (Rita) or *A* (Andrew).

1 I've got a big nose. [A]

2 I've got glasses. [ ]

3 I've got long eyelashes. [ ]

4 I haven't got red hair. [ ]

5 I've got long hair. [ ]

6 I haven't got a long neck. [ ]

2 Describing someone

13 **Draw a picture of a man or a woman. Then describe him / her. Use words from the unit.**

Has he / she got blond / brown hair?
Has he / she got broad shoulders?
Has he / she got a round chin?

Pets

Animal body parts

1 Look and write.

tail   beak   wings   paws   ~~whiskers~~   feathers   claws   fur

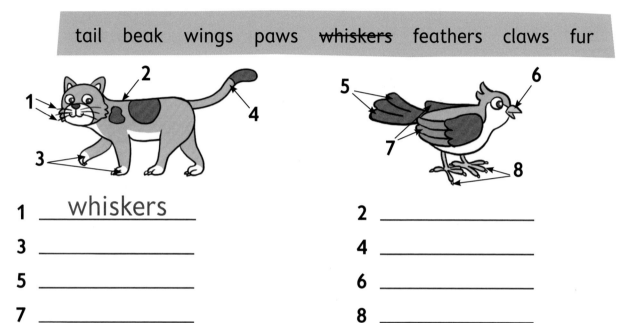

1 ___whiskers___

3 _____

5 _____

7 _____

2 _____

4 _____

6 _____

8 _____

2 Match the opposites.

1 smooth   **2** soft   **3** cute   **4** fast

a slow   **b** scary   **c** hard   **d** sharp

3 Unscramble. Then write.

Lifecycle of the butterfly

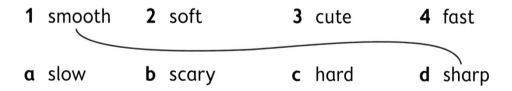

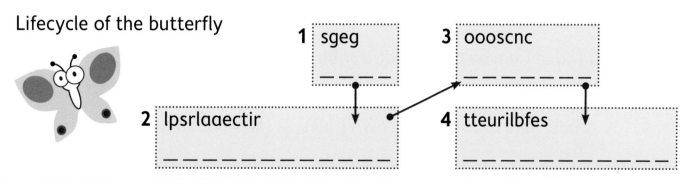

1 sgeg
_ _ _ _

2 lpsrlaaectir
_ _ _ _ _ _ _ _ _ _ _ _

3 oooscnc
_ _ _ _ _ _ _

4 tteurilbfes
_ _ _ _ _ _ _ _ _ _

What does it look like?

4 Read. Then match and write.

1

It's got wings.
It hasn't got feathers.
It's got six legs.
It's different colours.

2

It's got two feet
and it's got claws.
It's different colours.
It's got a tail.
It hasn't got four legs.

3

It's green.
It hasn't got fur or
hair. It's got four long
legs.

4

It's got a lot of fur
and long whiskers.
It's got a small
white tail and very
big ears.

a

b

c

d

It's a butterfly.

_____

_____

_____

5 Read. Then circle.

1 Have (*he* / *you*) got a pet?

2 Yes I (*have* / *haven't*). I've got a rabbit.

3 What (*does* / *do*) it look like?

4 My rabbit (*has* / *have*) got brown paws. It (*has* / *have*) got long ears.

6 Look and answer.

	tortoise	hamster	rabbit	snake	parrot
Ben	✗	✗	✗	✔	✗
Peter	✗	✔	✔	✗	✗
Gemma	✔	✔	✗	✗	✔
Pamela	✔	✗	✔	✗	✔

1 Has Peter got a rabbit and a tortoise?

No, he hasn't. He's got a rabbit and a hamster.

2 Has Pamela got a snake?

_____

3 Have Peter and Gemma got hamsters?

_____

4 Has Ben got a rabbit?

_____

5 Has Peter got two pets?

_____

7 Look again at Activity 6. Then write four true sentences.

1 Ben has got a snake.

2

3

4 _____

Emma's got a rabbit

8 Look. Then circle.

Emma   Paul

1 Emma (*has got* / *hasn't got*) a rabbit. She (*'s got* / *hasn't got*) a snake.

2 Paul (*has got* / *hasn't got*) a parrot. He (*'s got* / *hasn't got*) two frogs.

3 Emma (*has got* / *hasn't got*) a dog and Paul (*has got* / *hasn't got*) a dog.

4 Emma (*has got* / *hasn't got*) two cats and a parrot.

5 They (*'ve got* / *haven't got*) a fish. They (*'ve got* / *haven't got*) two dogs.

9 Look at Activity 8. Read and complete. Use words from the box.

> cats   has   ~~got~~   wings   has   hasn't

This is Emma and Paul. They've ¹ __got__ lots of pets. Emma has got five pets and Paul ² _____ got five pets too. Paul has got a dog and Emma ³ _____ got a dog. The parrot has got ⁴ _____ and a beak. It's a beautiful bird. The ⁵ _____ have got long whiskers. The snake ⁶ _____ got whiskers.

10 Read. What is Bip?

Bip is a _____.

Hi, Jenny!

Thank you so much for looking after Bip in August!
He's very good. Here are the instructions for him:

In the morning, take him out for a walk.

When you get back, please wash his paws if they
are dirty.

Give him some biscuits for breakfast.

Put more water in his water bowl.

Then put him in the garden.

In the afternoon, give him some meat and some
biscuits.

Take him out for a short walk.

He goes to bed at bedtime. Please put him in his bed.

Thank you!

Gemma xx

11 Read again. Then number the instructions in order.

▢ Put more water in his water bowl.

▢ Please put him in his bed.

▢ When you get back, please wash his paws if they are dirty.

▢ Then put him in the garden.

3 Giving instructions

We usually write instructions in order.

In the morning, take him out for a walk.

Then put him in the garden.

In the afternoon, take him for a walk.

12 Your friend is looking after your pet. Write instructions.

- What is your pet's name?

- When does he / she eat? What does he / she eat?

- What does he / she drink?

- Where and when does he / she go to sleep?

Dear _____,

Thank you for looking after _____

_____

_____

_____

_____

_____

_____

Home

Prepositions of place

1 Read. Then draw.

There's a bin below the table.
There's a cat behind the chair.
There's a tall plant next to
the table, on the right.
There's a small plant below
the window.
There's a dog in front
of the table.

2 Read. Then write.

1 You clean your teeth with this.   <u>toothbrush</u>

2 You wash your hair with this.   _____

3 This keeps you warm in bed.   _____

4 You put your clothes in this.   _____

5 You put your car in this.   _____

6 This is a place to sit outside.   _____

3 Find the words.

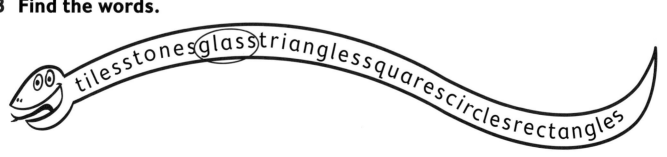

tilesstonesglasstrianglessquarescirclesrectangles

4 It's next to ...

4 Look and unscramble. Then write the answer.

1 TV / opposite / the / chair / the / Is

<u>Is the TV opposite the chair?</u>
<u>Yes, it is.</u>

2 the / plants / under / Are / window / the

_____

_____

3 Is / cat / on / the / window / the

_____

_____

4 the / Is / in / lamp / of / front / the / TV

_____

_____

5 Read the answer. Then write a question about your house.

1 <u>Is the TV next to the sofa?</u>　　Yes, it is.

2 _____　No, they aren't.

3 _____　Yes, they are.

4 _____　No, it isn't.

6 Read the letter. Then circle.

Hi Claire,

What does your new house look like? ((Is)/ Are) there a balcony?
(Is / Are) there any (plant / plants) on the balcony? I love plants!
(Is / Are) there a basement?
What does the garden look like? (Is / Are) it big? (Is / Are) there
a garage? (Is / Are) the car in the garage?
Send me a photo.
Love, Beth

7 Write a letter about your home. Use words from the box.

| wardrobe | plants | basement | bedrooms |
| picture | mirrors | big garden | garage |

_____

_____

_____

_____

_____

8 Look. Then write. Use the table.

There	is	a	plant(s)	in	the	TV
			wardrobe(s)	on		wardrobe
		two	sofa(s)	under		balcony
			lamp(s)	above		garden
		three	car(s)			garage
	are		food	opposite		basement
		lots of	table(s)	behind		cupboard
			chair(s)	next to		sofa
						chair
						table

1 There's a sofa next to the TV. _____

2 _____

3 _____

4 _____

5 _____

6 _____

9 Draw your classroom. Then write.

10 Read. Then circle.

House

This house is in a village, opposite the church. It's got four bedrooms. All the bedrooms have got wardrobes. There are mirrors in the bedrooms. There are two bathrooms. The bathrooms have got a mirror and a shower. Outside, there's a garage for two cars and a big garden.

Flat

This flat is in the centre of the town. It's next to the park. It's got two bedrooms and a bathroom. It hasn't got a garden but it's got a big balcony. The flat has got a garage in the basement of the building.

1 The house is (*next to /* *opposite*) the church.

2 The house (*has got / hasn't got*) a balcony.

3 In the house, there are wardrobes in the (*two / four*) bedrooms.

4 The flat is (*next to / opposite*) the park.

5 The flat (*has / hasn't*) got a basement.

11 Read again. Then write (✔).

	House	Flat
1 It's got four wardrobes.	✔	
2 There's one bathroom.		
3 It has got a balcony.		
4 It's next to the park.		
5 There's a big garden.		
6 It's got two bedrooms.		

4 Describing a house

12 **Write about a house or flat.**

- Where is it? What is next to / opposite it?

- How many bedrooms has it got? What is in them?

- Has it got a garden or balcony? Where is it? What's in / on it?

- Is there a garage?

Clothes

Clothes

5

1 Match the two parts of the word. Then write.

baseball		suit	tracksuit
track		form	_____
sweat		shirt	_____
uni		hat	_____
train		ers	_____

2 Draw and colour. Then write. Use words from the box.

> beanie   hiking boots   brown   colourful   jumper   leather   orange
> plain   red   scarf   dress   tights   woolly   sandals   baseball hat

1

cold

It's cold. I'm wearing _____
_____ .

2

hot

It's hot. I'm wearing _____
_____ .

3 Read the messages. Then answer.

> What are you wearing to Fran's party after school?

> I'm wearing black jeans, a brown leather belt and a red and white T-shirt.

> Are you wearing your new trainers?

> No, I'm not. I'm wearing my old white trainers. I love those trainers. What are you wearing?

> I'm wearing yellow and green shorts and I'm wearing a red hat. It's my favourite baseball hat. Is Jenny wearing new boots?

> Yes, she is. They are really nice. Okay. I've got Maths now. See you after school. Bye. Kate x

> Okay, bye. Becky x

1 What is Becky wearing to the party?

<u>She's wearing shorts and a hat.</u>

2 Is Kate wearing her new trainers?

_____

3 Is Jenny wearing her new boots?

_____

4 What is Kate wearing with her jeans?

_____

4 Unscramble the question. Then answer.

is / What / wearing / ? / Kate

_____

5 Read. Then write.

(old jeans) (~~a green T-shirt~~) (a brown beanie) (flip flops)

(a blue belt) (white sandals) (a woolly jumper) (cotton shorts)

This is ...	These are ...
a green T-shirt	

6 Read. Then circle.

1 (This is /(These are)) my new jeans.

2 (This is / These are) my favourite skirt.

3 This (is / are) my favourite blouse.

4 These are my brown (shorts / skirt).

7 Draw your favourite clothes. Then write. Use *this is* / *these are*.

_____

_____

_____

_____

_____

_____

_____

It's made from ...

8 Draw. Then write.

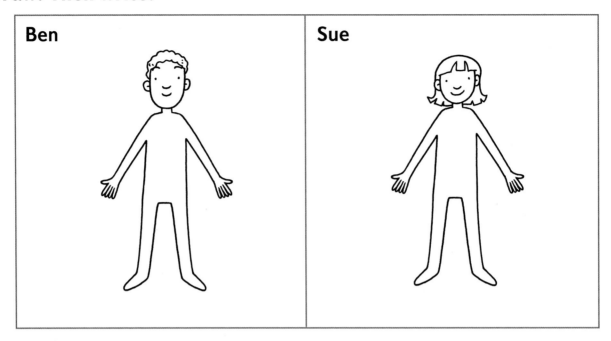

| Ben | Sue |

Ben <u>is wearing</u> _____

_____

Sue <u>is wearing</u> _____

_____

9 Read. Then complete. Use words from the box.

| made   is   's   ~~am~~   ~~wearing~~   're   black   from |

I ¹ <u>am</u>   ² <u>wearing</u> a brown leather jacket.

What a great T-shirt! It ³_____ ⁴_____ from cotton.
It's blue and white.

Georgie ⁵_____ wearing ⁶_____ trousers.
They ⁷_____ made ⁸_____ cotton.

10 Read the list. Write (✔) what you need to go on holiday.

toothbrush		trainers	
shorts		T-shirt	
butterfly		sofa	
comb		jeans	
rock		belt	

11 Read. Then draw what's missing.

~~woolly jumper~~
hiking boots
colourful ski jacket
jeans
plain scarf
socks
blue cotton T-shirt
leather belt
hat

5 Clothes

12 Read. Then correct.

1 I've got trousers grey.

I've got grey trousers.

2 I've got a hat woolly.

_____

3 I've got a white socks.

_____

4 I've got T-shirt cotton.

_____

13 Write a list of things you need to sleep at your friend's house. Then draw.

Sports, exercise

1 Write.

| climb | play | ride | do | catch |

_____ _____ _____ _____ _____

2 Read. Then match the pairs.

1 basketball   a pool
2 bowling   b court
3 swimming   c track
4 skating   d alley
5 running   e rink
6 ski   f slope

3 Unscramble. Then write.

| runt | ~~tcserth~~ | stiwt | dnbe |

1 S t r e t c h your arms.   2 _ _ _ _ _ your knees.
3 _ _ _ _ _ _ your body to the left.   4 _ _ _ _ around.

can / can't

4 Look. Then answer.

Class survey of different sports

	Do taekwondo	Play tennis	Play football	Play volleyball
Kim			██	██
Jason			██	██
Jemma		██	██	██
David	██	██	██	██

1 Can Kim play tennis?

<u>No, she can't. She can play volleyball.</u>

2 Can David play football?

_____

3 Can Jemma do taekwondo?

_____

4 How many children can play tennis?

_____

5 Can all the children play volleyball?

_____

5 Write about you. What sports can or can't you do?

_____

_____

_____

6 Look. Then write sentences. Use the prompts.

Me	gym	✘	skating rink	✔
My dad	stadium	✔	beach	✘
My best friend	ski slope	✘	gym	✔
My aunt	house	✘	park	✔
My mum	gym	✔	kitchen	✘
My teacher	football pitch	✘	beach	✔

1 <u>I wasn't at the gym. I was at the skating rink.</u>

2 My dad _____

3 My best friend _____

4 My aunt _____

5 _____

6 _____

7 Complete the table.

Last weekend, I was …	Last weekend, I wasn't …

6 Stretch your arms

8 Read and draw or write.

1 (Stretch your arms up.)

2 (Bend your knees.)

3 (_____)

4 (Twist your body to the right.)

5 (_____)

6 (Jump.)

9 Read about the sports day. Circle four more mistakes.

Parkhill School sports day

When	What	Who	Where
09.00	volleyball	Reds v Yellows	on the beach
10.00	basketball	Blues v Yellows	basketball court in the gym
11.30	tennis	Greens v Reds	tennis court
12.15	running (100 metres)	All	track in stadium

End of year sports day news

It's the last week and it's sports day. The day starts with volleyball. Reds are playing Yellows (in the gym) at 9.00. The basketball game is in the stadium at 10.00. Blues and Yellows are playing. The third sport is tennis. That's on the basketball court at 11.30. Greens are playing Yellows. The fourth sport is the 100 metres. That's on the beach at 12.15. Everyone is running.

10 Read again. Then correct.

1 The volleyball game is on the beach.

2 _____

3 _____

4 _____

5 _____

Remember!

play tennis   go swimming   do taekwondo

11 Read. Then write. Use words from the box.

> basketball   football   karate   running   skating   skiing
> swimming   taekwondo   tennis   volleyball

I love playing ...   I love going ...   I love doing ...

basketball

_____   _____   _____

_____   _____   _____

_____   _____   _____

12 Write about a sports day. Then write a news bulletin.

Sports day programme

What   Where

_____   _____

_____   _____

_____   _____

SPORTS DAY NEWS

_____

_____

_____

Food

Food plurals

1 Write the plural.

1 potato ___potatoes___   **2** cherry _____

3 carrot _____   **4** mango _____

5 avocado _____   **6** orange _____

2 Read and sort. Then write. Use words from the box.

Fruit	Vegetables
apricots	

apricots cabbage carrots
cucumber lettuce papaya
peaches spinach
strawberries watermelon

3 Look. Find these words.

dairy fats
grains healthy
protein sugars
unhealthy

H	G	R	A	I	N	S	T	Y	O	S	D
P	H	L	R	Y	U	U	D	C	B	I	K
R	E	A	Y	J	K	G	U	F	A	T	S
B	A	O	P	C	D	A	B	H	K	I	W
S	L	D	H	G	P	R	O	T	E	I	N
L	T	E	L	F	E	S	A	J	K	E	O
G	H	C	I	D	A	I	R	Y	L	C	P
S	Y	B	S	T	W	U	E	T	R	A	U
H	U	N	H	E	A	L	T	H	Y	O	F
D	O	E	S	A	D	F	W	R	C	P	O

7 Do you like ...?

4 Read and ✔ or ✘. Then write questions and answers.

spinach	✔	strawberries	☐
lettuce	☐	mangoes	☐
tomatoes	☐	peaches	☐

1 <u>Do you like spinach?</u>   <u>Yes I do.</u>

2 _____   _____

3 _____   _____

4 _____   _____

5 _____   _____

6 _____   _____

5 Unscramble. Find the questions and answers.

1 broccoli / I / do / Do / like / you / Yes

_____?

_____.

2 like / No / Sam / doesn't / Does / he / apricots

_____?

_____.

3 Yes / Tina / cherries / does / she / Does / like

_____?

_____.

6 Read. Then complete.

Is there
any fish?

Today's menu
rice
broccoli
carrots
potatoes
chicken
fish

any pears?

_____
_____
any cheese?

any potatoes?

7 Read the answers. Look at Activity 6. Then write the questions.

1 Is there any fish?_____

Yes, there is.

2 _____

No, there isn't.

3 _____

No, there aren't.

4 _____

Yes, there are.

some ... / lots of ...

8 Read and sort the food into *some* and *lots of*. Then write.

~~plums~~ ~~lettuce~~ cucumber beans broccoli cabbage oranges
mangoes apricots avocados papayas cherries

There is some ...	There are lots of ...
lettuce	plums

9 Read. Then unscramble and write.

1 lots / on / There / potatoes / are / the / table / of
There are lots of potatoes on the table.

2 in / is / fridge / cabbage / the / There / some

_____

3 lots / on / of / are / plate / peaches / the / There

_____

4 some / the / There / in / pan / is / fish

_____

10 What's your favourite food? Write.

_____

_____

11 Look at the menu. Then circle.

TODAY'S MENU

Salads

Potato and tomato salad   ☺   ☹

Green salad   ☹   ☹

Avocado and lettuce salad   ☺   ☺

Pizzas

Cheese and tomato   ☺   ☺

Broccoli, spinach and egg   ☺   ☹

Cheese and mushroom   ☹   ☺

Desserts

Strawberries and ice cream   ☺   ☺

Fruit salad with mango, papaya,
peaches and cherries   ☹   ☺

1 Does he like green salad?   _Yes / (No)_

2 Do they like cheese and tomato pizza?   _Yes / No_

3 Do they like avocado and lettuce salad?   _Yes / No_

4 Does she like strawberries and ice cream?   _Yes / No_

5 Does she like cheese and mushroom pizza?   _Yes / No_

7 A menu

12 Write a menu for a party. Use words from the unit.

- What foods do your friends like?
- What don't they like?
- Is there any special food?

Party menu

_____

_____

_____

_____

_____

_____

_____

_____

_____

Things we do

Actions, adverbs of manner

1 Look and match. Draw the missing pictures.

1 reading　　　　　**2** drinking　　　　　**3** walking

4 listening to music　　**5** sleeping　　　　**6** cleaning

a 　　b　　c

d 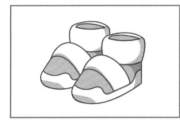　　e 　　f

2 Read. Then write the opposite.

1 I don't like playing the piano quietly.

I like playing the piano _____.

2 I don't like walking slowly. I _____.

_____.

3 Read. Then match.

1 do　　　　**a** the piano

2 play　　　**b** to music

3 listen　　**c** homework

4 clean　　**d** my shoes

8 What are you doing?

4 Read. Then answer.

1 What are Jane and Sue doing? (*read / library*)

<u>They are reading in the library.</u>

2 What is Tom doing? (*play football / stadium*)

_____

3 What is Karen doing? (*watch TV / living room*)

_____

4 What are you doing now?

_____

5 Look. Then write.

 my sister   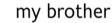 my brother

my dad   my grandparents

1 sister, read <u>My sister is reading a book in the bedroom.</u>

2 brother, wash _____

3 dad, drink _____

4 grandparents, listen to music _____

6 Read and complete.

1   Are you playing the violin? No, I am not.

2   _____ (do / homework)

3   _____ John _____? (sing / loudly)

4   Yes, he _____.

5   _____? (you / dance)

7 Find the mistakes. Then correct.

1   I is playing on my computer in my bedroom.
    I am playing on my computer in my bedroom.

2   It are raining outside.

    _____

3   Mum reading the book.

    _____

4   Dad are walking in the park.

    _____

5   Grandad is sleep in his chair.

    _____

6   My dog is play with a ball.

    _____

What are you doing?

8 Draw you and your friends. Then write. What are you doing? Use words from the box.

watch   play   wash   drink   clean   sleep   eat   walk   run   dance
read   make   quickly   loudly   quietly   slowly   terribly

_____

_____

_____

_____

_____

9 Which one is not correct? Read then circle.

1 I'm reading a book. / I'm write a story. / Mum is eating.

2 Jo is watching TV. / Jo and Tom are dancing. / Jo are playing football.

3 Dad is washing the car. / Mum are doing taekwondo. / I'm sleeping on the sofa.

10 Read. What instrument is Ann playing?

Ann is playing the _____.

Mum: Is that you, Ann?

Ann: Yes, Mum.

Mum: What are you doing?

Ann: I'm in the kitchen.

Mum: You're making a lot of noise!

Ann: Oh, sorry. I'm washing the dishes. There are no glasses!

(Ten minutes later ...)

Mum: Where are you, Ann?

Ann: I'm in my bedroom. I'm doing my homework.

Mum: Mmm ... Are you playing the trumpet?

Ann: Yes. And doing my homework. I've got music homework.

Mum: Well, please play quietly.

Ann: OK, Mum.

11 Read again. Then circle.

1 In the kitchen, Ann is (*washing the dishes* / *drinking*).

2 There are no clean (*pots* / *glasses*).

3 In her bedroom, Ann is doing her (*English* / *music*) homework.

4 Ann is playing (*quietly* / *loudly*).

5 Mum wants Ann to (*play loudly* / *play quietly*).

Remember!

Making words ending in -ing:

dance ➜ dancing   live ➜ living

12 Read. Then put the conversation in the order.

Susan is doing her homework in the living room. Jane is sitting next to Susan. She's listening to music and dancing. Susan can't do her homework. Jane is playing music loudly and Susan wants her to be quiet.
Mum is in the kitchen. She's washing the dishes.
Now Susan is in the kitchen, too. She's talking to Mum. Mum and Susan want Jane to go to her bedroom!

1	**Mum:**	What are you doing, Susan?
☐	**Mum:**	Jane, please listen to your music quietly, or go to your bedroom!
☐	**Mum:**	What are you doing, Jane?
☐	**Jane:**	I'm listening to music.
☐	**Susan:**	I'm doing my homework.
☐	**Jane:**	OK, Mum. Sorry, Susan
☐	**Susan:**	Jane is listening to music, and dancing! I can't do my homework.